This is
my photo

My name is

....

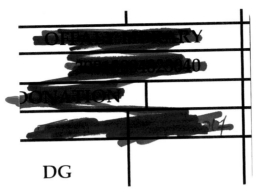

DG

The Story of Sarah

First published in 2004
Revised edition published 2008

Childnames.net
27 Villarea Park, Glenageary, Co. Dublin, Ireland
info@childnames.net
www.childnames.net
Tel +353 87 936 9888

Written by Eithne Diamond and John Gallagher

Illustrations by Stella Kearns
Additional illustrative input by DVD

Further illustrative input,
layout and pre-press: Ferret on the Dartboard

ISBN 978-1-906326-29-6

Design by DVD
Printed in China by Ming Tai Printing Co Ltd

For Conor and Sadhbh
ED and JG

For Kate Janaki (Ella) and Dara Luca
SK

The Story of Sarah

Eithne Diamond and John Gallagher

Illustrations: Stella Kearns

Childnames.net

Sarah :
the facts for big people

- The name Sarah, also spelled Sara, is derived from the Hebrew, meaning 'princess of all'.

- In the Bible and the Koran, Sarah is the long-time wife of Abraham, who after many years longing for a child finally conceives in very old age, providing the inspiration for our story.

- Sarah is one of the most developed female characters in the Bible.

- The story tells of a woman who, unable to have a child herself, accepts the 'custom' that her husband marries a slave girl, although any subsequent children count as her own.

- Sarah later evicts the slave girl, who returns to the household after God promises to look after her.

- Sarah herself conceives in very old age following the apparition of an angel. The Koran records her as at first laughing, then stating: "Woe is me. Shall I bear a son when old … this truly would be marvellous".

• Tradition says that she was buried by Abraham in a cave near Hebron in Israel.

• The depiction of Sarah's life in the Old Testament provides interesting insights into womens' position in middle-eastern society during Biblical times.

• It shows womens' ability to influence developments at family and extended family level and the complicated familial arrangements of that era.

• Her story is featured in television soap-like detail in the Book of Genesis 11-12, 15,16-18, 20-21. She is also mentioned in the Koran, Sura XI, 74-78.

• Sarah is linked to the Irish name Saraid, meaning 'best' or 'noble.'

• In Celtic mythology she is an ancestress of the kings of Scotland and the daughter of Conn of the Hundred Battles, ancestor of the Irish kings.

• Saraid was aunt of Cormac Mac Airt, an early king of Tara and the subject of numerous Fenian cycle stories.

• Sarah is also used to anglicize the Irish name Sorcha, which means 'bright' or 'radiant.'

• A first-century St Sarah is the patron saint of gypsies. Tradition says she was an Egyptian servant who was cast adrift in a boat and eventually found refuge in France.

• Famous modern-day bearers of the name include Sarah Ferguson, Duchess of York and actress Sarah Jessica Parker, star of the movie 'The First Wives Club' and the TV series 'Sex and the City'.

• Sarah Bernhardt was a French actress of the silent movie era who is commemorated in the Hollywood Walk of Fame.

• Sarah Vaughan was an American jazz singer.

Sarah :

the story for little people

O nce there was a girl named Sarah. She had long golden hair and a pretty smile.

Sarah always wore a bracelet on her right arm. "That's because I'm a big girl now," she would say to her mum. "I'm nearly as big as you and you always wear your jewellry on your right arm."

Sarah had lots of toys.
Whenever her relations
came to visit they
brought her presents.

Sarah had one pink teddy, two furry rabbits, three
fluffy tigers and four long-haired rag dolls.
She had a doll's house and a doll's buggy.

Sarah had a very big book on dinosaurs, which her uncle gave her for her birthday. One day her big brother took it to his room. "Mummy, Mummy, Tom's taken my dinosaur book," she said.

She didn't really mind, however, because she thought dinosaurs were a bit stupid and ugly and were really for boys anyway.

One thing Sarah didn't have was a dolly. Well, not a real dolly. She had her rag dolls. She had dolls with faces made of cloth. She had a doll which her auntie brought from another country. It wore funny clothes and had a wooden head.

Her mum said it must live on top of the cabinet because it was really an ornament and not a doll. "What's an ornament?" Sarah asked.

Once she climbed up on the shelves of the cabinet to get the doll, but it was too high to reach. Then Sarah could not get down again. "Mummy, Mummy, I'm stuck!" she called.

Sarah wanted a real doll that would close its eyes when she put it to bed. One she could dress in the baby clothes that her mum kept at the bottom of the press in her room.

"We might need those again some day," her mum would say.

19

When Sarah visited her friends they all had dolls that fitted nicely into a buggy.

She wanted a doll that would fit in her buggy, just like all her friends' dolls.

Nobody gave her one. 'If I don't get one soon I will be too old!' she thought.

"I want a doll for Christmas," she told her mum. She was sure she would get one.

23

On Christmas morning she ran downstairs. Under the Christmas tree was the most beautiful doll Sarah had ever seen. She was dressed in the finest clothes, with lace and ribbons. Her hair was tied with a silken bow. Sarah took it in her arms and gave it a big hug.

Then she suddenly noticed it was not the same as her friends' dolls either. It was a porcelain doll. Her face was shiny, hard and cold. Its eyes stared straight ahead. When Sarah put the doll down she did not close her eyes, but looked at the ceiling.

"It's lovely," thought Sarah, "but it's not a real doll."

Sarah was very sad every time she visited her friends'
houses and played with their real dolls.

"Soon I'll be too old and I will probably get a serious
present like a computer," she thought.

Then one morning in spring Sarah woke up early. She looked at the end of her bed and rubbed her eyes. She jumped down to look more closely. 'Can it be true?' she thought.

Sarah picked up her new doll. At once it closed its eyes. Yes, it was a real doll at last, like the one she always wanted. She held it in her arms.

"Happy birthday to you," sang her mum. "I hope you're not too old to enjoy another dolly. Would you have preferred a computer?"

Sarah just smiled.

What's in a name?
– more facts for big people

- When actress Betty Joan Perske was given the screen name Lauren Bacall one of the most popular first names for girls of recent decades was created.

- *The name Keira did not exist until the 21st century, except as a misspelling!*

- It is soaring up the baby name charts due to the success of UK-born actress Keira Knightly. She changed the spelling from Kiera to avoid mispronunciation in Hollywood.

- *Today there are thousands of first names. Even the most popular names may account for only 2–3% of the overall total.*

- There were far fewer names in previous centuries. Baptism registers in the UK during the second half of the 16th century record that one in five boys was named William.

- *During the second half of the 18th century, just three names – Elizabeth, Mary and Anne – accounted for 57% of all girls born in the UK.*

- As recently as the early 20th century, some first names were so common in Ireland that a second 'first' name was added for identification, often based on a parent's first name: hence the character Paidín Mike in Synge's famous play 'The Playboy of the Western World.'

- *In the north of England, until the late 19th century, many people relied on multiple names to convey family identity – for instance, Tom o'Dick o'Mary's.*

- Today's parents increasingly use original and inventive first names as a means of conveying identity and 'brand' to their children.

- *Back in the 16th century, however, the Council of Trent ruled that Catholics could name their children only after canonised saints or angels.*

- During the same period, in Britain and USA the Puritans insisted that only names from the Bible were valid. They later allowed names such as Livewell and Safe-on-high.

- *Without any edicts, the double name John Paul suddenly became popular in Ireland after the Pope visited the country in 1979.*

- From the 13th to the 15th century it was common to give the same name to more than one child in a family: the second would be known, for example, as John the younger.

- *The name Jesus is highly popular in Spanish-speaking countries, but considered sacrilegious in much of northern and central Europe.*

- Changing a person's name was once a grave offence. Records in the English city of Rochester state that on Oct 15th, 1515, an Agnes Sharpe 'voluntarily changed the name of her infant son … for which she submitted penance.'

- *Many names still originate from religious history, such as Cate, Katie and Kate from Saint Catherine.*

- How a name is spelled can have religious links also. Sarah is a favourite for Christians, while Sara is preferred by Muslims.

- *The popular boy's name Aaron emerged as a variation of the Biblical Aron, thanks to Elvis Aaron Presley.*

- A name from Irish legend, Conor, has recently become popular internationally but it is often spelled Connor, which denotes a surname in Ireland!

- *Lawrence (Latin), Chloe (Greek literature) and Victoria (history) are examples of other sources for names.*

- Then there's Jack! It seems to have emerged from nowhere – but perhaps from Jankin, a version of John – to become the ubiquitous name of fairy tales and a highly-popular first name.

- *Name 'globalisation' gives us monikers like Tanya, Brooklyn and Chelsea.*

- The general decrease in formality – nobody is now known as Mr, or Mrs, Jones – leads parents to seek ever more imaginative and unique names.

- *Names popular in one country may hardly exist elsewhere. Ever heard of Seren or Cerys? Both are Top 20 names for girls in Wales.*

- Copying celebrities is popular. In 2000 Sonny Sandoval, singer with American group POD, mentioned on MTV that he had named his daughter Nevaeh ('Heaven' backwards). By 2005 more than 3,000 girls were given the name each year in the USA.

- *Finally, before opting for the latest new fab name, it would be both wise and humorous to take a listen to the Johnny Cash song 'A Boy Named Sue.'*

Christening ... Birthdays ... Christmas ...

We'll post your order to you!

Order books from this series
for postal delivery
to **anywhere in the world**.

- **Credit card bookings**:
  click the 'Purchase' link on *www.childnames.net* and follow the steps.

- **Order by post**:
  check the postage costs to your country and the accepted payment methods
  on *www.childnames.net*, then forward the total amount, with the name of
  the book(s) required and your postal address, to:

Childnames.net, **27 Villarea Park**, **Glenageary**, **Co Dublin**, **Ireland**.

A personalised 'My name is ...' poster for your child!

- visit *www.childnames.net*
- click on 'Posters'
- select from a range of illustrations ...
- and follow the links.

Please note:

This service is available by
mail order only (posters are
not available in bookshops).